INSTRUMENTAL PLAY-ALONG

SHOW TUN

CW00407633

Contents

TITLE	PAGE	CD TRACK
Any Dream Will Do	2	1
Bring Him Home	3	2
Can't Help Lovin' Dat Man	4	3
The Candy Man	5	4
Climb Ev'ry Mountain	6	5
Dancing Queen	7	6
Don't Cry For Me Argentina	8	7
The Impossible Dream (The Quest)	9	8
My Favorite Things	10	9
The Phantom Of The Opera	12	10
Where Is Love?	16	11
Written In The Stars	14	12
B♭ Tuning Notes		13

HOW TO USE THE CD ACCOMPANIMENT:
A melody cue appears on the right channel only. If your CD player has a balance adjustment, you can adjust the volume of the melody by turning down the right channel.

Exclusive Distributors:
Music Sales Limited
14-15 Berners Street, London W1T 3LJ, UK.

Order No. HLE90003144
ISBN 13: 978-1-84609-599-3
This book © Copyright 2007 Hal Leonard Europe

Printed in the USA

Your Guarantee of Quality
As publishers, we strive to produce every book to the highest commercial standards. The book has been carefully designed to minimise awkward page turns and to make playing from it a real pleasure. Throughout, the printing and binding have been planned to ensure a sturdy, attractive publication which should give years of enjoyment. If your copy fails to meet our high standards, please inform us and we will gladly replace it.

www.musicsales.com

 HLE

HAL LEONARD EUROPE
DISTRIBUTED BY MUSIC SALES

◆ ANY DREAM WILL DO

from JOSEPH AND THE AMAZING TECHNICOLOR® DREAMCOAT

Clarinet

Music by ANDREW LLOYD WEBBER
Lyrics by TIM RICE

❷ BRING HIM HOME
from LES MISÉRABLES

Clarinet

Music by CLAUDE-MICHEL SCHÖNBERG
Lyrics by ALAIN BOUBLIL and HERBERT KRETZMER

❸ CAN'T HELP LOVIN' DAT MAN

from SHOW BOAT

Lyrics by OSCAR HAMMERSTEIN II
Music by JEROME KERN

Clarinet

◆ THE CANDY MAN
from WILLY WONKA AND THE CHOCOLATE FACTORY

CLARINET

Words and Music by LESLIE BRICUSSE
and ANTHONY NEWLEY

♦ CLIMB EV'RY MOUNTAIN

from THE SOUND OF MUSIC

Clarinet

Lyrics by OSCAR HAMMERSTEIN II
Music by RICHARD RODGERS

◆ DANCING QUEEN

from MAMMA MIA

Words and Music by BENNY ANDERSSON,
BJORN ULVAEUS and STIG ANDERSON

Clarinet

◆ DON'T CRY FOR ME ARGENTINA

from EVITA

Words by TIM RICE
Music by ANDREW LLOYD WEBBER

CLARINET

❽ THE IMPOSSIBLE DREAM
(The Quest)
from MAN OF LA MANCHA

CLARINET

Lyric by JOE DARION
Music by MITCH LEIGH

◆9 MY FAVORITE THINGS

from THE SOUND OF MUSIC

Clarinet

Lyrics by OSCAR HAMMERSTEIN II
Music by RICHARD RODGERS

◆❿THE PHANTOM OF THE OPERA

from THE PHANTOM OF THE OPERA

Music by ANDREW LLOYD WEBBER
Lyrics by CHARLES HART
Additional Lyrics by RICHARD STILGOE and MIKE BATT

CLARINET

⑫ WRITTEN IN THE STARS

from Walt Disney Theatrical Productions' AIDA

CLARINET

Music by ELTON JOHN
Lyrics by TIM RICE

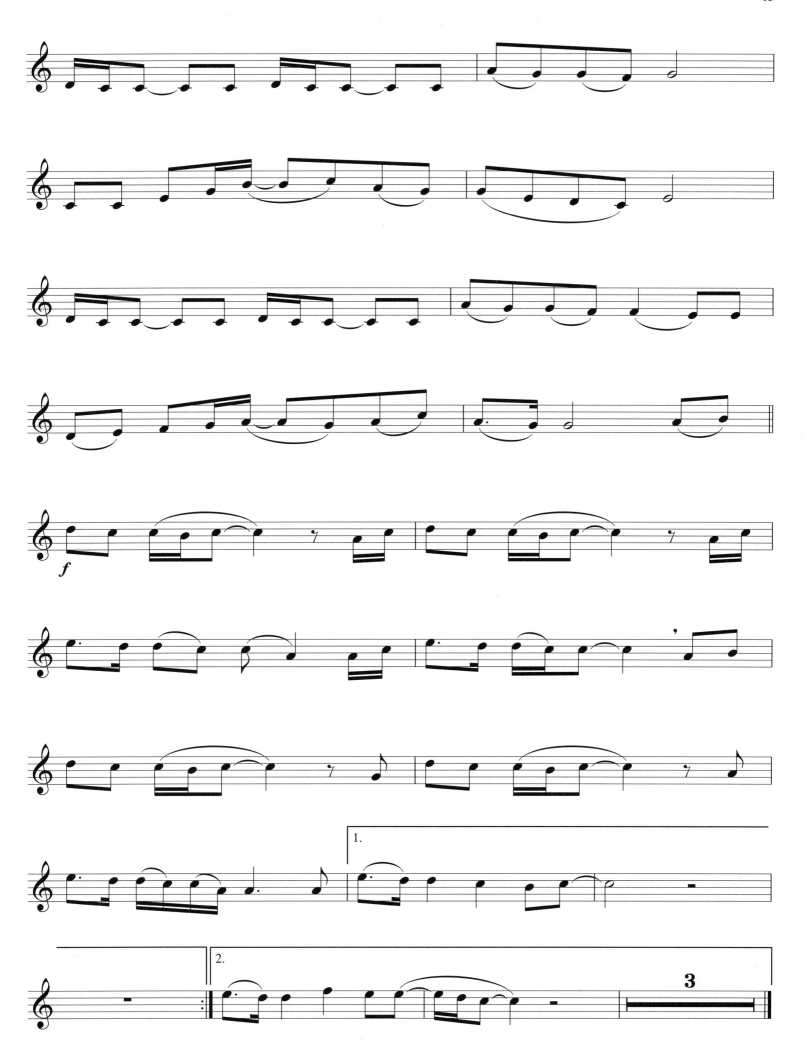

WHERE IS LOVE?

from OLIVER!

Words and Music by
LIONEL BART

CLARINET